Baguette to grips with KS2 French!

This smashing CGP French Question Book is perfect for helping pupils
aged 9-10 build up their basic French skills. It's packed with
fun and engaging practice for the whole of Year 5!

Each topic starts with an introduction to the vocabulary they'll
need, and all the answers are at the back of the book.

There's also free online audio to help pupils fine-tune their
pronunciation of all the key vocab. You'll find it here:

www.cgpbooks.co.uk/KS2French

What CGP is all about

Our sole aim here at CGP is to produce the highest quality books
— carefully written, immaculately presented and
dangerously close to being funny.

Then we work our socks off to get them out to you
— at the cheapest possible prices.

Contents

Contents

Section 5 — Seasons

Section 6 — The Environment

Published by CGP

Editors:
Keith Blackhall, Robbie Driscoll, Jack Tooth
With thanks to Ben Merritt and Gabrielle Richardson for the proofreading.
With thanks to Jan Greenway for the copyright research.
Thumb illustration used throughout the book © iStock.com.

ISBN: 978 1 78908 354 5

Clipart from Corel®
Printed by Elanders Ltd, Newcastle upon Tyne.
Based on the classic CGP style created by Richard Parsons.

Section 1 — On Holiday

Où vas-tu en vacances?	

Where are you going on holiday?

Learn to answer this question by saying where you are going on holiday:

Où vas-tu en vacances?   Where are you going on holiday?

Je vais...   ...en France.
I'm going...   ...to France.

...en Espagne.
...to Spain.

...en Italie.
...to Italy.

...en Allemagne.
...to Germany.

...en Grèce.
...to Greece.

...aux États-Unis.
...to the USA.

...en Chine.
...to China.

...au pays de Galles.
...to Wales.

1 **Complete the crossword by writing each word in French.**

Across:

4. USA

6. Greece

7. Germany

8. Spain

Down:

1. Wales

2. China

3. France

5. Italy

Don't forget about the capital letters in the crossword.

© CGP — not to be photocopied

2 **Fill in the missing letters to complete the sentences below.**

Je vais en | E | | | | | | | .

Je vais en | | | l | | | g | | .

Je vais en | | | | | | e | .

Je vais aux | | t | | t | | – | | | | | .

Je vais en | | | è | | | .

3 **Rewrite these sentences using the correct spaces, capital letters and punctuation.**

oùvastuenvacances

....

jevaisaupaysdegalles

....

Write down what each sentence means in English.

....

....

"I can say where I'm going on holiday."

| Tu loges où? | **_Where are you staying?_**  |

Answer this question by saying where you're staying on your holiday:

Tu loges où?   Where are you staying?

Je loge dans...   I'm staying in...   ...une caravane.   ...a caravan.

You might also want to tell someone how long you're going away for:

Qu'est-ce que tu fais pour les vacances?
What are you doing for the holidays?

Je passe...   ...deux semaines dans...   ...un hôtel.
I'm spending...   ...two weeks in...   ...a hotel.

'One week' is 'une semaine'.

...un appartement.
...an apartment.

...une auberge de jeunesse.
...a youth hostel.

...un gîte.
...a holiday cottage.

...une tente.
...a tent.

...un camping-car.
...a campervan.

...une station de ski.
...a ski resort.

...une ferme.
...a farm.

---

(1) **Read the statements in the boxes, then answer the questions below.**

| Je passe une semaine dans un gîte.
— Rachel | Je passe trois semaines dans un hôtel.
— Alima | Je passe deux semaines dans un camping-car.
— Bailey |

Where is Alima staying? ....

How long is Bailey's holiday? ....

Who is staying in a holiday cottage? ....

Who is going on the longest holiday? ....

2 Circle the correct word to complete each sentence.

Je **loge** / **passe** dans un camping-car.

Je loge dans une **station** / **auberge** de jeunesse.

Je passe une **semaine** / **semaines** dans un hôtel.

Je loge dans une **appartement** / **ferme** .

Je passe trois semaines dans **un** / **une** caravane.

Je passe deux semaines dans une **hôtel** / **tente** .

3 Fill in the gaps in this conversation using the correct words from the box.

loges   fais   station   semaines   vacances   dans   appartement

Qu'est-ce que tu ....
pour les .... ?

Je passe deux ....
dans une .... de ski.

Tu .... où?

Je loge ....
un ....

"I can say where I'm staying and for how long."

Au zoo	At the zoo

Practise answering this question by saying what you saw at the zoo:

Qu'est-ce que tu as vu au zoo?   What did you see at the zoo?

J'ai vu...   I saw...   ...un perroquet.   ...a parrot.

You might also want to say which animal at the zoo is your favourite:

Quel est ton animal préféré au zoo?
What is your favourite animal at the zoo?

Mon animal préféré est...   ...un éléphant.
My favourite animal is...   ...an elephant.

...un tigre.
...a tiger.

...une girafe.
...a giraffe.

...un rhinocéros.
...a rhinoceros.

...un pingouin.
...a penguin.

...un singe.
...a monkey.

...un lion.
...a lion.

...un ours.
...a bear.

1 **Fill in the gaps in the sentences below to match each picture.**

J'ai vu ....

J'ai vu ....

J'ai vu ....

2 Read the sentences in the boxes. Then tick to say whether the statements are <u>true</u> or <u>false</u>.

| Au zoo, j'ai vu un perroquet et une girafe, mais mon animal préféré est un pingouin.
— Ayaz | Mon animal préféré est un lion. Au zoo, j'ai vu une girafe et un ours.
— Sébastien | Au zoo, j'ai vu un singe et un éléphant. Mon animal préféré est un singe.
— Mia |

	True	False
Ayaz saw his favourite animal at the zoo.	☐	☐
Three people saw a giraffe at the zoo.	☐	☐
Mia's favourite animal is a monkey.	☐	☐
No one saw a bear at the zoo.	☐	☐

3 Write the sentences below in French.

What did you see at the zoo?

....

What is your favourite animal at the zoo?

....

....

My favourite animal is a rhinoceros.

....

....

"I can talk about the animals at the zoo."

À la plage	At the beach 

Make sure you can understand this question about the beach:

Qu'est-ce qu'il y a à la plage?
What is there at the beach?

To answer, you need to use the phrase '<u>il y a</u>'.
'Il y a' can mean both '<u>there is</u>' and '<u>there are</u>':

Il y a...   ...un crabe.   Il y a...   ...des vagues.
There is...   ...a crab.   There are...   ...some waves.

...du sable.   ...un bateau.   ...un requin.   ...une glace.
...some sand.   ...a boat.   ...a shark.   ...an ice cream.

...un surfeur.   ...un château de sable.   ...une mouette.
...a surfer.   ...a sandcastle.   ...a seagull.

(1) **Put a tick in the boxes next to the words that are spelt correctly.**
Put a cross in the boxes next to the words that are spelt incorrectly.

un surfer ☐   un château ☐   la plage ☐

une glase ☐   des vauges ☐   du sabel ☐

Write the correct spellings for the words that are spelt incorrectly.

[ ]

2 Fill in the gaps in the sentences below to match each picture.

Il y a ....

Il y a ....

Il y a ....

Il y a ....

3 Write the question and answer below in French.

What is there at the beach?

There is a sandcastle and an ice cream.

....

....

....

....

"I can describe what there is at the beach."

Au parc d'attractions	**At the theme park**

The answers to this question are all things you can find at a theme park:

Qu'est-ce qu'il y a au parc d'attractions?
What is there at the theme park?

Il y a...   There is...   ...une grande roue.   ...a big wheel.

...un manège.
...a carousel.

...un train fantôme.
...a ghost train.

...un pédalo.
...a pedalo.

...des montagnes russes.
...a rollercoaster.

...un toboggan aquatique.
...a water slide.

...de la barbe à papa.
...some candy floss.

...une maison hantée.
...a haunted house.

...un bateau pirate.
...a pirate ship.

1 **Look at the picture below. Put a tick in the boxes next to the things that are in the picture, and a cross in the boxes next to the things that aren't.**

une grande roue ☐   un pédalo ☐   une maison hantée ☐

un bateau pirate ☐   un manège ☐   de la barbe à papa ☐

2 Fill in the missing letters to complete the sentences below.

Il y a un ⬚⬚⬚⬚⬚⬚⬚[n] aquatique.

Il y a un train ⬚⬚⬚[t]⬚⬚ .

Il y a de la ⬚⬚[r]⬚⬚ à ⬚⬚⬚⬚ .

Il y a un [b]⬚⬚⬚⬚⬚ pirate.

Il y a une ⬚⬚⬚⬚⬚[n] hantée.

3 Unscramble each set of words to make a sentence.

parc ? qu' y attractions au il est-ce d' Qu' a

....

....

y montagnes Il . a russes des

....

Write down what each sentence means in English.

....

....

"I can describe what there is at the theme park."

| Je commande une boisson | **I'm ordering a drink**  |

If you want to order a drink in France, learn how to answer this question:

Qu'est-ce que vous désirez?   What would you like?

Je voudrais...   ...un café.
I would like...   ...a coffee.

...un thé.
...a tea.

...un chocolat chaud.
...a hot chocolate.

...un jus d'orange.
...an orange juice.

...une limonade.
...a lemonade.

...un coca.
...a cola.

...une eau minérale.
...a mineral water.

1 Look at the drinks menu and read the statements in the boxes. Then fill in the gaps by writing down how much money each person needs.

coffee – £1   lemonade – £2

cola – £3   hot chocolate – £4

Je voudrais un coca et un café.
— Lottie

Je voudrais un café et une limonade.
— Callum

Je voudrais un chocolat chaud.
— Hafsa

Lottie needs £ ....   Callum needs £ ....   Hafsa needs £ ....

2 Fill in the gaps in the sentences below by writing the French for the English word(s) in brackets.

Qu'est-ce que .... désirez? (**you**)

Je .... un coca. (**would like**)

Je voudrais un .... (**coffee**)

Je voudrais une .... minérale. (**water**)

Je voudrais un .... chaud. (**chocolate**)

Je voudrais un .... (**tea**)

Je voudrais .... limonade. (**a**)

Je voudrais un jus d'................................... . (**orange**)

3 Unscramble each set of words to make a sentence.

désirez   que   ?   Qu'   vous   est-ce

....

une   minérale   voudrais   .   Je   eau

....

Write down what each sentence means in English.

....

....

"I can say what I would like to drink."

Section 2 — Eating Out

Chez le glacier | ## At the ice cream shop

Ordering an ice cream works just like ordering a drink:

Qu'est-ce que vous désirez?   What would you like?

Je voudrais...   ...une glace à la framboise.
I would like...   ...a raspberry ice cream.

It's useful to be able to say how many scoops you'd like:

Je voudrais...   ...une boule de...   ...glace à la fraise.
I would like...   ...one scoop of...   ...strawberry ice cream.

Je voudrais...   ...deux boules de...   ...glace au chocolat.
I would like...   ...two scoops of...   ...chocolate ice cream.

...une glace au caramel.
...a caramel ice cream.

...une glace à la vanille.
...a vanilla ice cream.

...une glace à la menthe.
...a mint ice cream.

...une glace à la banane.
...a banana ice cream.

1 **Circle the correct word to complete each sentence.**

Je voudrais une glace **à** / **au** chocolat.

Je voudrais une glace au **caramel** / **caramelle** .

Je voudrais une glace à la **vanil** / **vanille** .

Je voudrais une **boule** / **boules** de glace à la banane.

Je voudrais deux boules de glace **à** / **au** la framboise.

2 Read the statements in the boxes, then write in the table how many scoops of each ice cream each person wants. The first one has been done for you.

Je voudrais deux boules de glace à la banane.
— Polly

Je voudrais une boule de glace à la fraise et une boule de glace au chocolat.
— Raul

Je voudrais une boule de glace au chocolat et deux boules de glace à la banane.
— Hakim

Je voudrais une boule de glace à la fraise.
— Grace

Polly	0	2	0
Raul			
Hakim			
Grace			

3 Imagine you are working in a French ice cream shop and a customer comes in. Write down the question you would ask to find out what they would like.

....

The customer wants two scoops of mint ice cream. How would they say this in French?

....

....

"I can say what ice cream I would like."

Au marché	At the market

At the market, you might want to say how much food you would <u>like</u>:

Qu'est-ce que vous désirez?   What would you like?

Je voudrais...   ...cent grammes...   ...de champignons.
I would like...   ...one hundred grams...   ...of mushrooms.

Sometimes, you might also be asked how much of something you <u>need</u>:

De quoi avez-vous besoin?   What do you need?

J'ai besoin de...   ...deux cents grammes...   ...de tomates.
I need...   ...two hundred grams...   ...of tomatoes.

If the word after 'de' begins with a <u>vowel</u>, then 'de' is shortened to '<u>d</u>'':

J'ai besoin d'...   ...une barquette...   ...de fraises.
I need...   ...a punnet...   ...of strawberries.

...un kilo...	...un demi-kilo...	...un sac...
...a kilo...	...half a kilo...	...a bag...

(1) Milo's mum has sent him to buy some food at the market. Look at Milo's shopping list, then fill in the gaps in the sentences in English.

> • un kilo de tomates
> • cent grammes de fraises
> • un demi-kilo de champignons

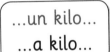

Milo's mum wants .... of mushrooms.

Milo's mum wants .... of tomatoes.

Milo's mum wants .... of strawberries.

2 Fill in the gaps in the sentences below to match each picture.

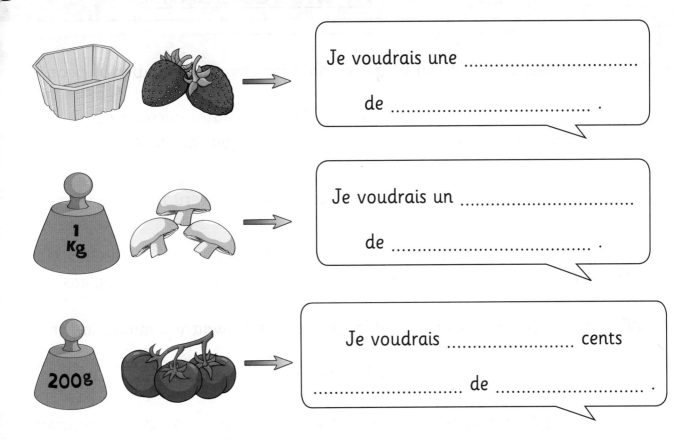

Je voudrais une ....

de ....

Je voudrais un ....

de ....

Je voudrais .... cents

.... de ....

3 Write the question and answer below in French.

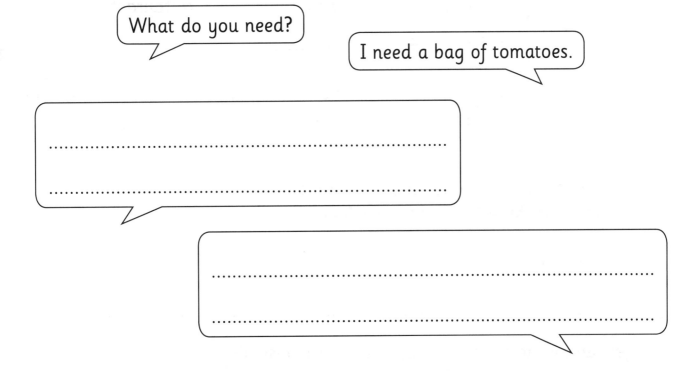

What do you need?

I need a bag of tomatoes.

....

....

....

....

"I can ask for a specific amount of something."

Section 2 — Eating Out

Au restaurant	**At the restaurant** 

At a restaurant, you'll need to get a table for the right number of people:

Vous désirez...
Would you like...

...une table pour quatre personnes?
...a table for four people?

Oui, merci beaucoup.   Yes, thank you very much.

Non, je voudrais...
No, I would like...

...une table pour deux personnes...
...a table for two people...

...s'il vous plaît.
...please.

When the food arrives at the table, the waiter or waitress might say this:

Bon appétit!   Enjoy your meal!

The answers to this question are all useful words for a visit to a restaurant:

Qu'est-ce que c'est?   What is it?

C'est...   It's...   ...un restaurant.   ...a restaurant.

...un café.
...a café.

...une carte.
...a menu.

...un serveur.
...a waiter.

...une serveuse.
...a waitress.

...l'addition.
...the bill.

(1) **Rewrite these sentences using the correct spaces, capital letters and punctuation.**

cestladdition

....

jevoudraisunetablepourtroispersonnessilvousplaît

....

....

2) Complete the crossword by writing each word in French.

Across:

3. café

4. restaurant

5. waiter

Down:

1. waitress

2. bill

3. menu

3) Write the sentences below in French.

Would you like a table for two people?

....

....

Yes, thank you very much.

....

No, I would like a table for four people.

....

....

Enjoy your meal!

....

"I can talk about restaurants and ask for a table."

Je prends...	**I'll have...**

Answer this question to order food or drink in a restaurant:

Qu'est-ce que vous prenez comme...   ...entrée?
What are you having for your...   ...starter?

Je prends...   I'll have...   ...la soupe.   ...the soup.

Make sure you can say what other people's orders are too:

Qu'est-ce qu'il prend comme entrée?   Il prend la soupe.
What is he having for his starter?   He'll have the soup.

Qu'est-ce qu'elle prend comme entrée?   Elle prend la soupe.
What is she having for her starter?   She'll have the soup.

...plat principal?   ...dessert?   ...boisson?
...main course?   ...dessert?   ...drink?

...la pizza.   ...le gâteau.   ...un jus d'orange.
...the pizza.   ...the cake.   ...an orange juice.

1 **Match each question to the correct answer.**

Qu'est-ce que vous prenez comme boisson?

Elle prend la pizza.

Qu'est-ce qu'il prend comme entrée?

Je prends un jus d'orange.

Qu'est-ce qu'elle prend comme plat principal?

Il prend la soupe.

2 Unscramble each set of words to make a sentence.

vous ? est-ce entrée que comme Qu' prenez

....

....

soupe . prends la Je

....

Write down what each sentence means in English.

....

....

3 Write answers to the questions below to match each picture.

Qu'est-ce qu'elle prend comme dessert?

....

....

Qu'est-ce qu'il prend comme boisson?

....

....

"I can order food and drink in a restaurant."

Section 3 — Hobbies

| Mes passe-temps | <u>**My hobbies**</u> |

Use this question and answer to talk about what you <u>like</u> or <u>dislike</u> doing:

Tu aimes...   Do you like...   ...le sport?   ...sport?

Oui, j'aime...   Non, je n'aime pas...   ...le sport.
Yes, I like...   No, I don't like...   ...sport.

When you really like or really dislike something, you can use <u>love</u> or <u>hate</u>:

Tu aimes...   Do you like...   ...la musique?   ...music?

Oui, j'adore...   Non, je déteste...   ...la musique.
Yes, I love...   No, I hate...   ...music.

...la natation.   ...le cyclisme.   ...la lecture.   ...les jeux vidéo.
...swimming.   ...cycling.   ...reading.   ...video games.

1   **Match each sentence to the correct face, then to the correct picture.**

Je n'aime pas la musique.

Je déteste le cyclisme.

J'aime la natation.

J'adore la lecture.

2 Read the sentences in the boxes. Then tick to say whether the statements are <u>true</u> or <u>false</u>.

> Je déteste la natation.
> — Jean

> J'adore le cyclisme et la natation.
> — Antoni

> Je n'aime pas la lecture, mais j'aime la musique.
> — Céline

> J'aime le sport, mais j'adore les jeux vidéo.
> — Rosa

	True	False
Rosa likes video games more than sport.	☐	☐
Two people like swimming.	☐	☐
Céline likes reading and music.	☐	☐
Antoni loves cycling and swimming.	☐	☐

3 Imagine you want to know if your friend likes video games. Write down a question you would ask in French to find out.

....

Your friend replies: "Non, je déteste les jeux vidéo." Write down what this means in English.

....

"I can say what hobbies I like and don't like."

Section 3 — Hobbies

| La musique | # Music |

If someone asks if you like a type of music, it's good to be able to say more than just 'yes' or 'no'. Here's how to go into more detail:

Tu aimes... ...la musique classique?
Do you like... ...classical music?

'Classique' can be replaced by 'pop', 'rock' or 'folk' — these mean the same thing in English and French.

Oui, j'aime la musique classique...
Yes, I like classical music...

...mais je préfère la musique pop.
...but I prefer pop music.

You can also explain <u>why</u> you like or dislike a certain type of music:

Tu aimes... ...la musique rock?
Do you like... ...rock music?

Oui, c'est... ...super! Non, c'est... ...nul!
Yes, it's... ...great! No, it's... ...rubbish!

...entraînant! ...ennuyeux! ...énervant!
...catchy! ...boring! ...annoying!

1 **Colour in the rest of the boxes needed to spell out these words in French.**

rubbish

| n | e | a | n | r | b | u | a | c | m | l | e |

annoying

| é | u | n | e | a | r | b | v | a | r | n | t |

boring

| e | o | n | a | n | u | y | v | e | m | u | x |

great

| s | o | u | h | w | p | s | e | g | l | r | k |

2 Fill in the gaps in this conversation using the correct words from the box.

> Tu   musique   entraînant   la   Non   aimes   folk

.... aimes .... musique .... ?

.... , c'est ennuyeux!

Tu .... la .... rock?

Oui, c'est .... !

3 Write the question and answer below in French.

Do you like pop music?

Yes, I like pop music, but I prefer classical music.

....
....

....
....

"I can tell people what type of music I like."

| Les instruments de musique | **Musical instruments** |

You might be asked if you play a musical instrument:

Tu joues d'un instrument de musique?
Do you play a musical instrument?

If you don't play a musical instrument, you can answer like this:

Non, je ne joue pas d'un instrument de musique.
No, I don't play a musical instrument.

If you do play an instrument, this is how you say what you play:

Oui, je joue...   Yes, I play...   ...du piano.   ...the piano.

...du violon.
...the violin.

...de la flûte.
...the flute.

...de la guitare.
...the guitar.

...de la batterie.
...the drums.

...du saxophone.
...the saxophone.

...de la clarinette.
...the clarinet.

...de la trompette.
...the trumpet.

1 **Complete the crossword by writing each word in French.**

Across:

1. guitar

3. violin

5. clarinet

6. drums

Down:

2. trumpet

4. flute

You don't need the 'du' or 'de la' bit for this one.

2 **Rewrite these sentences using the correct spaces, capital letters and punctuation.**

tujouesduninstrumentdemusique

....

....

ouijejouedelaclarinette

....

nonjenejouepasduninstrumentdemusique

....

....

3 **Imagine you have asked these people what musical instrument they play. Write down how you would expect them to answer in French.**

....
....

....
....

....
....

"I can say what musical instrument I play."

| Le weekend | # The weekend |

To ask people what they do at the weekend, and to say what you do, learn this question and all of the answers:

Qu'est-ce que tu fais le weekend?
What do you do at the weekend?

Je fais du trampoline.
I go on the trampoline.

You don't need any extra words to say '<u>at</u> the weekend' — it's just 'le weekend'.

Je vais au parc.
I go to the park.

Je regarde la télé.
I watch TV.

Je surfe sur le net.
I surf the internet.

Je vais au cinéma.
I go to the cinema.

Je joue aux jeux vidéo.
I play video games.

Je téléphone à mes amis.
I call my friends.

Je joue aux jeux de société.
I play board games.

(1) **Fill in the gaps in the sentences below using the correct words from the box.**

You should only use each word from the box <u>once</u>.

| regarde | joue | surfe | fais | vais |

Qu'est-ce que tu .... le weekend?

Je .... sur le net.

Je .... aux jeux de société.

Je .... au cinéma.

Je .... la télé.

2 Read the statements in the boxes, then answer the questions below.

> Le weekend, je surfe sur le net et je fais du trampoline.
> — Anabelle

> Le weekend, je vais au parc et au cinéma.
> — Lucinda

> Je regarde la télé et je téléphone à mes amis.
> — Olivier

> Je joue aux jeux de société ou je vais au cinéma.
> — Sylvain

Who does Olivier call? ....

Where does Lucinda go? ....

Who plays board games? ....

What does Anabelle do? ....

....

3 Write the sentences below in French.

What do you do at the weekend?

....

I go to the cinema and I play video games.

....

....

At the weekend, I call my friends.

....

"I can talk about what I do at the weekend."

Section 3 — Hobbies

| Les films | # Films |

You might be asked if you want to watch a particular type of film:

> Tu veux regarder...
> Do you want to watch...

> ...un film d'action?
> ...an action film?

Here's how to answer this question, whether it's a 'yes' or a 'no':

> Oui, je veux regarder...
> Yes, I want to watch...

> ...un film d'action.
> ...an action film.

> Non, je ne veux pas regarder...
> No, I don't want to watch...

> ...un film comique.
> ...a comedy film.

> ...un dessin animé.
> ...a cartoon.

> ...un film d'horreur.
> ...a horror film.

> ...un film d'aventure.
> ...an adventure film.

> ...un film romantique.
> ...a romantic film.

(1) **Match each sentence to the correct picture.**

> Je veux regarder
> un film romantique.

> Je veux regarder
> un film comique.

> Je veux regarder
> un film d'aventure.

2 Circle the words you need to write these sentences in French.

Do you want to watch a cartoon?

Tu   animer   film
regardé   je   veux   ne
un   la   une
regarder   animé   dessin

I don't want to watch an action film.

Je   le   d'horreur
un   une   film   de
action   veux   pas
ne   d'action   regarder

Use the circled words to write the English sentences in French.

Do you want to watch a cartoon?

....

I don't want to watch an action film.

....

....

3 A friend asks you: "Tu veux regarder un film d'horreur?"
Write down what this means in English.

....

You want to tell them that you don't want to watch a horror film. Write down what you would say in French.

....

....

"I can say what type of film I want to watch."

       Section 3 — Hobbies

Section 4 — A School Trip

| Les roues du bus | **The wheels on the bus** |

Learn this question and answer to describe what you can hear on the bus:

Qu'est-ce que tu entends?   What do you hear?

J'entends...   ...les essuie-glaces.
I hear...   ...the windscreen wipers.

...le bus.
...the bus.

...le bébé.
...the baby.

...le klaxon.
...the horn.

...le moteur.
...the engine.

...les gens.
...the people.

...les roues.
...the wheels.

(1) **Fill in the missing letters to complete the sentences below.**

J'entends le [ ][l][ ][ ][ ][ ] .

 J'entends les [ ][ ][ ][ ][s] .

J'entends le [ ][ ][ ][ ][u][ ] .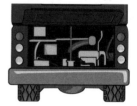

 J'entends les [g][ ][ ][ ] .

2 **Rewrite these sentences correctly by unscrambling the underlined words.**

Qu'est-ce que tu **sntedne**?

....

J'entends **sle siseeu-cgesla** et **el ébéb**.

....

Write down what each sentence means in English.

....

....

....

3 **Write the question and answer below in French.**

What do you hear?

I hear the bus and the horn.

....

....

....

....

"I can describe the sounds I hear on the bus."

En route	**On the way**

This is how to say what activities you like doing when you're on the bus:

> Qu'est-ce que tu aimes faire dans le bus?
> What do you like to do on the bus?

J'aime...   I like...   ...chanter.   ...to sing.

You can also talk about what you would like to do during a bus journey:

> Qu'est-ce que tu voudrais faire pendant le voyage?
> What would you like to do during the journey?

Je voudrais...   I would like...   ...lire.   ...to read.

...dormir.
...to sleep.

...manger des bonbons.
...to eat sweets.

...bavarder avec mes amis.
...to chat with my friends.

...jouer aux jeux vidéo.
...to play video games.

...rêver.
...to daydream.

...écouter de la musique.
...to listen to music.

1 Circle the correct word to complete each sentence.

Qu'est-ce que tu **aime** / **aimes** faire dans le bus?

J'aime bavarder **avec** / **aveque** mes amis.

Je **voudrais** / **voudrait** manger des bonbons.

J'aime jouer **aux** / **au** jeux vidéo.

Je voudrais **dormer** / **dormir** .

J'aime **réver** / **rêver** .

2 Read what these people like to do on the bus, then tick to say whether the statements are <u>true</u> or <u>false</u>.

> J'aime chanter et écouter de la musique.
> — Natalie

> J'aime jouer aux jeux vidéo et lire.
> — Alexandre

> J'aime bavarder avec mes amis et chanter.
> — Salman

	True	False
Alexandre likes to read on the bus.	☐	☐
Natalie likes to listen to music on the bus.	☐	☐
Only one person likes to sing on the bus.	☐	☐

3 Write the question that goes with each answer.

....

....

Pendant le voyage, je voudrais manger des bonbons.

....

....

Dans le bus, j'aime bavarder avec mes amis.

"I can say what I like doing on the bus."

Section 4 — A School Trip

| À travers la vitre | **Through the window** |

Learn how to say what you can see through the window during a journey:

Qu'est-ce que tu vois?   What do you see?

Je vois...   ...un camion.
I see...   ...a lorry.

...une ville.
...a town.

...un oiseau.
...a bird.

...un moulin.
...a windmill.

...une vache.
...a cow.

...un arbre.
...a tree.

...un feu tricolore.
...traffic lights.

...une boîte aux lettres.
...a post box.

...une cabine téléphonique.
...a telephone box.

1 **Fill in the missing letters to complete the sentences below.**

 Je vois un c

 Je vois une □□□□ e .

 Je vois un □□ b □□ .

2 **Complete the crossword by writing each word in French.**

You don't need the 'un' or 'une' bit for this one.

Across:

1. cow

5. bird

6. town

Down:

2. tree

3. windmill

4. lorry

3 **The sentences below all have a mistake in them.
Rewrite the sentences, correcting the mistakes.**

Qu'est-que ce tu vois?

....

Je voit un feu tricolore.

....

Je vois une cabin téléphonique.

....

Je vois une boîte au lettres.

....

"I can say what I see through the window."

Section 4 — A School Trip

Au musée	**At the museum**

Practise answering this question by saying what there is at the museum:

Qu'est-ce qu'il y a au musée?
What is there at the museum?

Remember — 'il y a' can mean either 'there is' or 'there are'.

Il y a...
There is...

...une momie.
...a mummy.

Il y a...
There are...

...des pièces en or.
...some gold coins.

...une peinture.
...a painting.

...une armure complète.
...a suit of armour.

...une billetterie.
...a ticket office.

...des os de dinosaure.
...some dinosaur bones.

...des bijoux anciens.
...some ancient jewellery.

(1) **Match each sentence to the correct picture.**

Il y a une armure complète.

Il y a des bijoux anciens.

Il y a une peinture.

Il y a des os de dinosaure.

2 Circle the words you need to write these sentences in French.

There is a ticket office.

Il une office

le musée y

a des la

des au

billetterie

There are some gold coins.

Il le or les

sont une des

a ce y

en anciens pièces

Use the circled words to write the English sentences in French.

There is a ticket office.

....

There are some gold coins.

....

3 Imagine your friend has visited a museum and you want to know what there is at the museum. Write down a question you would ask in French to find out.

....

Your friend replies: "Il y a des bijoux anciens et une momie."
Write down what this means in English.

....

....

"I can say what there is at a museum."

| À la campagne | **In the countryside** |

Make sure you can talk about what you like doing in the countryside:

Qu'est-ce que tu aimes faire à la campagne?
What do you like to do in the countryside?

J'aime...   I like...   ...nager.   ...to swim.

You might want to describe what you're going to do when you're there:

Qu'est-ce que tu vas faire à la campagne?
What are you going to do in the countryside?

Je vais...   I'm going...   ...faire du cheval.   ...to ride a horse.

...faire un pique-nique.
...to have a picnic.

...jouer à la balle.
...to play catch.

...nourrir un agneau.
...to feed a lamb.

...dessiner.
...to draw.

...ramasser des feuilles.
...to collect leaves.

...ramasser des mûres.
...to collect blackberries.

1 Fill in the gaps in this conversation using the correct words from the box.

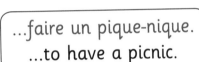

aimes   la   que   jouer   campagne

Qu'est-ce .... tu ....

faire à la .... ?

J'aime .... à .... balle.

2) These people are saying what they're going to do in the countryside. Read the statements in the boxes, then answer the questions below.

> Je vais dessiner et jouer à la balle.
> — Julien

> Je vais nager et nourrir un agneau.
> — Rory

> Je vais dessiner et ramasser des mûres.
> — Melissa

> Je vais ramasser des feuilles et faire un pique-nique.
> — Noor

Which two people are going to draw? ....

What is Rory going to do? ....

What is Melissa going to collect? ....

Who is going to have a picnic? ....

3) **Write the sentences below in French.**

What are you going to do in the countryside?

....

....

I'm going to ride a horse and draw.

....

I like to swim and collect leaves.

....

....

"I can talk about countryside activities."

| Les saisons | ## The seasons |

Learn to answer this question by saying what season it is:

> C'est quelle saison?
> What season is it?

> C'est...
> It's...

> ...le printemps.
> ...spring.

‿ You need to put '**le**' or '**l'**' before a season, even if you're not saying '**the**' in English.

You need to know the words for some periods of time too:

> Qu'est-ce que c'est?
> What is it?

> C'est...
> It's...

> ...une semaine.
> ...a week.

| ...l'été. | ...l'automne. | ...l'hiver. | ...un mois. | ...une année. |
| ...summer. | ...autumn. | ...winter. | ...a month. | ...a year. |

1 **Match each sentence to the correct picture.**

> C'est l'hiver.

> C'est l'été.

> C'est le printemps.

> C'est l'automne.

2 Put a tick in the boxes next to the words that are spelt correctly.
Put a cross in the boxes next to the words that are spelt incorrectly.

l'iver ☐   un moi ☐   le printemps ☐

une année ☐   l'été ☐   une semane ☐

Write the correct spellings for the words that are spelt incorrectly.

3 The sentences below all have a mistake in them.
Rewrite the sentences, correcting the mistakes.

C'est un année.

....

C'est le hiver.

....

C'est automne.

....

4 Fill in the gaps in the sentences below using the correct period of time.

Il y a sept jours dans une ....

Il y a quatre semaines dans un ....

In French, the word 'jours' means 'days'.

Il y a douze mois dans une ....

"I can name the seasons."

| Le printemps et l'été | **Spring and summer** |  |

If someone asks why you like spring and summer, this is how to answer:

Pourquoi tu aimes...   ...le printemps?   ...l'été?
Why do you like...   ...spring?   ...summer?

Parce que j'aime...   ...faire des pique-niques.
Because I like to...   ...have picnics.

You might want to talk about what you can do in spring and summer:

Qu'est-ce que tu peux faire...   ...au printemps?   ...en été?
What can you do...   ...in spring?   ...in summer?

Je peux...   I can...   ...aller à la plage.   ...go to the beach.

...caresser les agneaux.
...stroke the lambs.

...voir les jonquilles.
...see the daffodils.

...jouer au parc.
...play in the park.

...manger une glace.
...eat an ice cream.

...manger des œufs de Pâques.
...eat Easter eggs.

---

1   **Circle the correct word to complete each sentence.**

Pourquoi / **Parce que** tu aimes l'été?

Parce que **j'aimes** / **j'aime** jouer au parc.

Qu'est-ce que tu peux faire **en** / **au** printemps?

Je **peux** / **peu** voir les jonquilles.

Je peux **mangé** / **manger** une glace.

Parce que j'aime aller **au** / **à la** plage.

2 Read the sentences in the boxes. Then tick to say whether the statements are true or false.

J'aime le printemps parce que j'aime jouer au parc et manger des œufs de Pâques.
— Yvonne

J'aime l'été parce que j'aime faire des pique-niques.
— David

J'aime le printemps et l'été parce que j'aime jouer au parc.
— Farouk

J'aime l'été parce que j'aime aller à la plage et manger une glace.
— Paulette

	True	False
Farouk likes to have picnics in spring and summer.	☐	☐
Paulette likes to go to the beach in summer.	☐	☐
David likes to have picnics in spring.	☐	☐
Yvonne and Farouk both like to play in the park.	☐	☐

3 Imagine you want to know what your friend can do in spring. Write down the question you would ask in French to find out.

....

....

Your friend replies: "Je peux caresser les agneaux."
Write down what this means in English.

....

"I can explain why I like spring and summer."

L'automne et l'hiver

Autumn and winter

Practise naming some of the things you'll see in autumn and winter:

Qu'est-ce que c'est?   What is it?

C'est...
It's...

...un renne.
...a reindeer.

Ce sont...
They're...

...des feuilles rouges.
...red leaves.

Here's a slightly different way of using the same words and phrases:

Qu'est-ce que tu peux voir...
What can you see...

...en automne?
...in autumn?

...en hiver?
...in winter?

Je peux voir...   I can see...

...une citrouille.   ...a pumpkin.

...une châtaigne.
...a chestnut.

...un cadeau.
...a present.

...un sapin de Noël.
...a Christmas tree.

...une boule de neige.
...a snowball.

...un bonhomme de neige.
...a snowman.

...un flocon de neige.
...a snowflake.

1 **Fill in the missing letters to complete the sentences below.**

C'est un | f | | | | | de neige. ⟵

C'est une | | | u | | de neige.

C'est un | | | | | | | | e | de neige. ⟵

2 Fill in the gaps in the sentences below to match each picture.

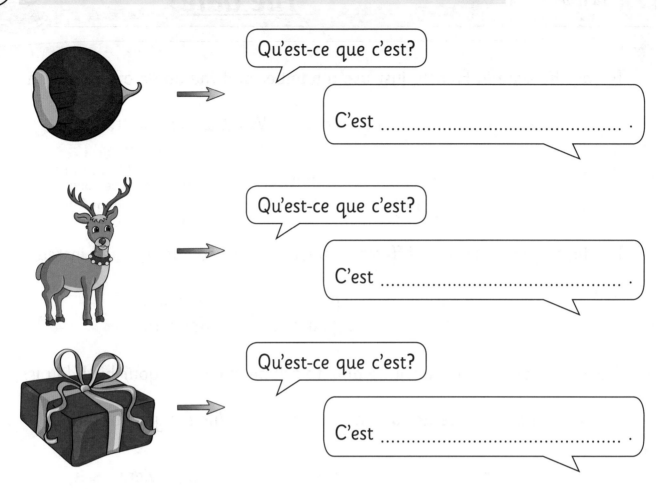

Qu'est-ce que c'est?

C'est ....

Qu'est-ce que c'est?

C'est ....

Qu'est-ce que c'est?

C'est ....

3 Write the sentences below in French.

What can you see in winter?

....

I can see a Christmas tree.

....

In autumn, I can see some red leaves and a pumpkin.

....

....

"I can say what I see in autumn and winter."

La date	**The date**

To say the date in French, just use a number and the name of the month:

> Quelle est la date d'aujourd'hui?   What is the date today?

On est le...	...cinq...	...janvier.
It's the...	...fifth of...	...January.

You can replace 'cinq' with any number from 2 to 31.

The first of the month is different. You'll need to say '<u>le premier</u>' instead:

On est le...	...premier...	...janvier.
It's the...	...first of...	...January.

Once you can do this, you'll be able to tell people when your birthday is:

> Quelle est la date de ton anniversaire?   When is your birthday?

C'est le...	...vingt-cinq...	...janvier.
It's the...	...twenty-fifth of...	...January.

...février. ...February.	...mars. ...March.	...avril. ...April.	...mai. ...May.	...juin. ...June.	...juillet. ...July.

...août. ...August.	...septembre. ...September.	...octobre. ...October.	...novembre. ...November.	...décembre. ...December.

1) **Rewrite these sentences using the correct spaces, capital letters and punctuation.**

quelleestladatedaujourdhui

....

onestledixseptnovembre

....

2 Circle the correct word to complete each sentence.

Quelle est la date de ton **aniversaire** / **anniversaire** ?

C'est le **neuf** / **neuve** janvier.

C'est le seize **fébrier** / **février** .

C'est le **vingt-trois** / **vinght-trois** mars.

C'est le **premier** / **première** juin.

C'est le douze **julliet** / **juillet** .

You'll need to be able to count up to 31 in French to complete Q2 and Q3.

3 Fill in the gaps in the sentences below to match each picture.

| 8 MAY | ⟹ On est le .... |

| 1 DEC | ⟹ On est le .... |

| 14 APR | ⟹ On est le .... |

| 31 OCT | ⟹ On est le .... |

| 24 AUG | ⟹ On est le .... |

| 20 SEP | ⟹ On est le .... |

"I can say the date and when my birthday is."

Section 5 — Seasons

Les travaux manuels	**Arts and crafts**

To celebrate Chinese New Year, people often make lanterns.
Make sure you can name the things you need to make one:

Qu'est-ce que c'est?   What is it?

C'est...   ...une règle.   Ce sont...   ...des ciseaux.
It's...   ...a ruler.   They're...   ...some scissors.

If you want to ask for something, here's one way to do it:

Qu'est-ce que tu voudrais?   What would you like?

Je voudrais...   I would like...   ...un crayon.   ...a pencil.

...des feutres.
...some felt-tip pens.

...une feuille A4.
...a sheet of A4 paper.

...du ruban adhésif.
...some sticky tape.

...une poignée.
...a handle.

...un lampion.
...a lantern.

(1) **Fill in the gaps in this conversation using the correct words from the box.**

Je	crayon	voudrais	des	que	feutres

Qu'est-ce .... tu .... ?

.... voudrais un .... et

....

2 Label the objects in the picture below in French.

Make sure you write the 'un', 'une', 'du' or 'des' bit.

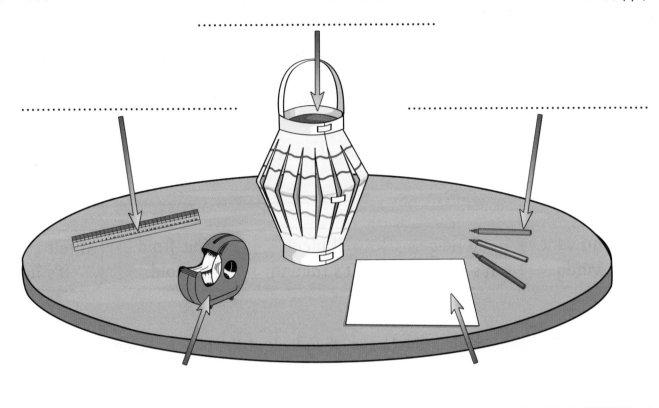

3 Prisha is at an arts and crafts shop and wants to buy some supplies. Read the speech bubble and write down what she is saying in English.

Je voudrais des ciseaux, une poignée, une règle et du ruban adhésif s'il vous plaît.

....

....

....

"I can ask for different arts and crafts items."

Section 6 — The Environment

| Le temps | ## The weather |

This is how you ask about the weather and say what the weather is like:

Quel temps fait-il?   What is the weather like?

Il y a du soleil.   It's sunny.

| Il y a du vent. It's windy. | Il neige. It's snowing. | Il pleut. It's raining. | Il fait froid. It's cold. | Il fait chaud. It's hot. |

1 **Read the statements in the boxes, then look at the picture below.**

Il y a du soleil mais il fait froid.
— Jenny

Il y a du soleil et il fait chaud.
— George

2°c

Who is correct? Jenny or George?

....

2 **Circle the correct word to complete each sentence.**

Il / **Il y a** du vent.

Il fait / **Il** neige.

Il y a / **Il** du soleil.

Il y a / **Il fait** chaud.

3 Look at the weather map of France, then fill in the gaps to complete the sentences below.

To say 'in' a town in French, you use the word 'à', e.g. 'in Marseille' is 'à Marseille'.

À Marseille, il .... du soleil.

À .... , ... pleut.

À .... , il neige.

À Bordeaux, il y a ....

4 Write the question and answer below in French.

What is the weather like?

It's raining and it's cold.

....

....

....

....

"I can say what the weather is like."

| L'étang | # The pond |

This is how to say what animals there are in a pond:

Qu'est-ce qu'il y a dans l'étang?   What is there in the pond?

Il y a...   ...un poisson.
There is...   ...a fish.

Here's another way to talk about animals in a pond:

Qui habite dans l'étang?   Who lives in the pond?

Un triton...   ...habite dans l'étang.
A newt...   ...lives in the pond.

Un crapaud...
A toad...

Un cygne...
A swan...

Une grenouille...
A frog...

Une libellule...
A dragonfly...

1 Fill in the missing letters to spell the words
below. Use the picture clues to help you.

| | | | p | | | |

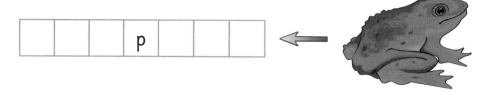

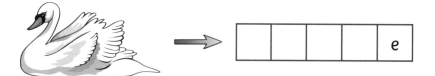

| | | | | e |

| t | | | | | |

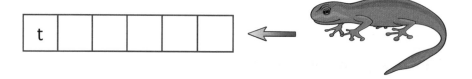

2 Write the question that goes with each answer.

....
....

Un crapaud habite dans l'étang.

....
....

Il y a une grenouille.

3 Circle the words you need to write these sentences in French.

There is a fish and a frog.

poisson   dans
      l'   y
         une
            grenouille
  a   Il   habite   la
    étang   un   le   et

A dragonfly lives in the pond.

Il   l'   est   étang
sont   Une   dans   y
      a
          la   grenouille
  en   libellule   habite

Use the circled words to write the English sentences in French.

There is a fish and a frog.

....

A dragonfly lives in the pond.

....

"I can talk about the animals in a pond."

Section 6 — The Environment

Le jardin	**The garden**

Practise telling people what animals there are in the garden:

Qu'est-ce qu'il y a dans le jardin?   What is there in the garden?

Il y a...   ...un hérisson.   ...une limace.   ...une araignée.
There is...   ...a hedgehog.   ...a slug.   ...a spider.

You may also want to say what each animal eats. To do this, change '<u>un</u>'
to '<u>le</u>' and '<u>une</u>' to '<u>la</u>'. If the animal starts with a vowel, use '<u>l</u>'' instead:

Le hérisson mange quoi?   What does the hedgehog eat?

Le hérisson...   ...mange...   ...la limace.   ...l'araignée.
The hedgehog...   ...eats...   ...the slug.   ...the spider.

...une chenille.	...un oiseau.	...un renard.	...une souris.	...une mouche.
...a caterpillar.	...a bird.	...a fox.	...a mouse.	...a fly.

(1) **Complete the crossword by writing each word in French.**

Across:

1. mouse

3. caterpillar

5. fly

6. spider

Down:

2. fox

4. slug

You don't need the 'un', 'une', 'le', 'la' or 'l'' bit for this one.

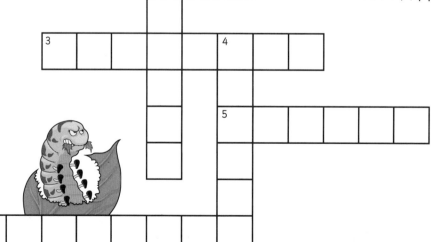

Look at the food chain, then write down what each animal eats in French. The first one has been started for you.

Le renard mange ....

Remember to use '**l'**' for animals that start with a vowel.

....

....

....

....

3) Write the sentences below in French.

What is there in the garden?

....

There is a hedgehog.

....

What does the bird eat?

....

The bird eats the caterpillar.

....

"I can talk about the animals in the garden."

Dans le jardin	# In the garden

Learn this way of saying what you like to do in the garden:

> Qu'est-ce que tu aimes faire dans le jardin?
> What do you like to do in the garden?

J'aime...   I like...   ...jouer au badminton.   ...to play badminton.

You might also want to tell people what you don't like to do:

> Qu'est-ce que tu n'aimes pas faire dans le jardin?
> What don't you like to do in the garden?

Je n'aime pas...   I don't like...   ...jouer au foot.   ...to play football.

...ramasser des insectes.
...to collect insects.

...planter des arbres.
...to plant trees.

...arroser les plantes.
...to water the plants.

...jouer avec mes animaux.
...to play with my pets.

...jouer dans le bac à sable.
...to play in the sandpit.

...lire.
...to read.

(1) Match each sentence to the correct picture.

Je n'aime pas jouer
au badminton.

Je n'aime
pas lire.

J'aime jouer dans
le bac à sable.

© CGP — not to be photocopie

2 Read the statements in the boxes, then answer the questions below.

> Dans le jardin, je n'aime
> pas jouer au foot ou
> ramasser des insectes.
> — Rachid

> Dans le jardin, j'aime jouer
> avec mes animaux, mais je
> n'aime pas planter des arbres.
> — Lola

What two things does Rachid not like doing in the garden?

....

What doesn't Lola like doing in the garden?

....

What does Lola like doing?

....

3 The sentences below all have a mistake in them.
Rewrite the sentences, correcting the mistakes.

Qu'est-ce que tu aime faire dans le jardin?

....

....

J'aime jouer du foot.

....

Je ne aime pas arroser les plantes.

....

"I can say what I like doing in the garden."

Section 6 — The Environment

Les ordures	**Rubbish**

To talk about recycling, you'll need to learn this vocabulary:

Qu'est-ce que c'est?   What is it?

C'est...   ...la poubelle à recyclage.
It's...   ...the recycling bin.

Learn how to say what you're throwing in the recycling bin:

Qu'est-ce que tu jettes dans la poubelle à recyclage?
What are you throwing into the recycling bin?

Je jette...   I'm throwing...   ...un bocal en verre.   ...a glass jar.

...un pot à yaourt.
...a yoghurt pot.

...une bouteille en plastique.
...a plastic bottle.

...une boîte vide.
...an empty tin.

...un journal.
...a newspaper.

...une canette à soda.
...a drinks can.

...un carton à céréales.
...a cereal box.

1 **Fill in the missing letters to complete the sentences below.**

C'est une ☐☐î☐☐ vide. (**tin**)

C'est un j☐☐☐☐☐☐☐ . (**newspaper**)

C'est un ☐☐☐☐☐l en verre. (**jar**)

C'est un carton à ☐☐r☐☐l☐☐ . (**cereal**)

2 Fill in the gaps in the sentences below to match each picture.

C'est la .... à ....

Je jette une .... en ....

Je .... un pot à ....

3 Unscramble each set of words to make a sentence.

jettes à Qu' tu recyclage ? dans est-ce poubelle que la

....

....

soda jette . une à Je canette

....

Write down what each sentence means in English.

....

....

....

"I can say what I'm throwing in the recycling bin."

Answers

Section 1 — On Holiday

Pages 4-5 — Where are you going on holiday?

1.

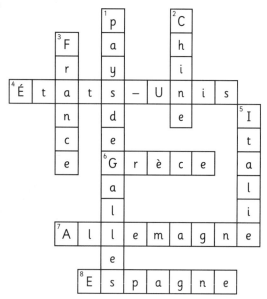

2. Je vais en E**spagne**.
   Je vais en **Allemagne**.
   Je vais en **Italie**.
   Je vais aux **États-Unis**.
   Je vais en **Grèce**.

3. **Où vas-tu en vacances?**
   Je vais au pays de Galles.

   Where are you going on holiday?
   I'm going to Wales.

Pages 6-7 — Where are you staying?

1. Where is Alima staying? **In a hotel**
   How long is Bailey's holiday? **Two weeks**
   Who is staying in a holiday cottage? **Rachel**
   Who is going on the longest holiday? **Alima**

2. Je **loge** dans un camping-car.
   Je loge dans une **auberge** de jeunesse.
   Je passe une **semaine** dans un hôtel.
   Je loge dans une **ferme**.
   Je passe trois semaines dans **une** caravane.
   Je passe deux semaines dans une **tente**.

3. Qu'est-ce que tu **fais** pour les **vacances**?
   Je passe deux **semaines** dans une **station** de ski.
   Tu **loges** où?
   Je loge **dans** un **appartement**.

Pages 8-9 — At the zoo

1. J'ai vu **un tigre**.
   J'ai vu **un ours**.
   J'ai vu **un éléphant**.

2. False, False, True, False

3. **Qu'est-ce que tu as vu au zoo?**
   Quel est ton animal préféré au zoo?
   Mon animal préféré est un rhinocéros.

Pages 10-11 — At the beach

1. You should have ticked: un château, la plage.
   You should have crossed: un surfer, une glase,
   des vauges, du sabel.
   The correct spellings are: **un surfeur, une glace, des vag**
   du sable.

2. Il y a **un requin**.
   Il y a **un bateau**.
   Il y a **une mouette**.
   Il y a **un crabe**.

3. **Qu'est-ce qu'il y a à la plage?**
   Il y a un château de sable et une glace.

Pages 12-13 — At the theme park

1. You should have ticked: une grande roue,
   un pédalo, un manège, une maison hantée.
   You should have crossed: un bateau pirate,
   de la barbe à papa.

2. Il y a un **tobogga**n aquatique.
   Il y a un train **fantôme**.
   Il y a de la **barbe** à **papa**.
   Il y a un b**ateau** pirate.
   Il y a une **maiso**n hantée.

3. **Qu'est-ce qu'il y a au parc d'attractions?**
   Il y a des montagnes russes.

   What is there at the theme park?
   There is a rollercoaster.

Section 2 — Eating Out

Pages 14-15 — I'm ordering a drink

1. Lottie needs £**4**.
   Callum needs £**3**.
   Hafsa needs £**4**.

2. Qu'est-ce que **vous** désirez?
   Je **voudrais** un coca.
   Je voudrais un **café**.
   Je voudrais une **eau** minérale.
   Je voudrais un **chocolat** chaud.
   Je voudrais un **thé**.
   Je voudrais **une** limonade.
   Je voudrais un jus d'**orange**.

3. **Qu'est-ce que vous désirez?**
   Je voudrais une eau minérale.
   What would you like?
   I would like a mineral water.

Pages 16-17 — At the ice cream shop

1. Je voudrais une glace **au** chocolat.
   Je voudrais une glace au **caramel**.
   Je voudrais une glace à la **vanille**.
   Je voudrais une **boule** de glace à la banane.
   Je voudrais deux boules de glace **à** la framboise.

. Polly — 0, 2, 0
Raul — **1**, **0**, **1**
Hakim — **0**, **2**, **1**
Grace — **1**, **0**, **0**

3. **Qu'est-ce que vous désirez?**
   Je voudrais deux boules de glace à la menthe.

Pages 18-19 — At the market

1. Milo's mum wants **half a kilo** of mushrooms.
   Milo's mum wants **a kilo** of tomatoes.
   Milo's mum wants **one hundred grams** of strawberries.

2. Je voudrais une **barquette** de **fraises**.
   Je voudrais un **kilo** de **champignons**.
   Je voudrais **deux** cents **grammes** de **tomates**.

3. **De quoi avez-vous besoin?**
   J'ai besoin d'un sac de tomates.

Pages 20-21 — At the restaurant

1. **C'est l'addition.**
   Je voudrais une table pour trois personnes s'il vous plaît.

2.

	s								a
	e		c	a	f	é			d
	r		a						d
	v		r						i
r	e	s	t	a	u	r	a	n	t
	u		e						i
	s								o
	s	e	r	v	e	u	r		n

3. **Vous désirez une table pour deux personnes?**
   Oui, merci beaucoup.
   Non, je voudrais une table pour quatre personnes.
   Bon appétit!

Pages 22-23 — I'll have...

1. You should have matched these questions and answers:
   Qu'est-ce que vous prenez comme boisson? — Je prends un jus d'orange.
   Qu'est-ce qu'il prend comme entrée? — Il prend la soupe.
   Qu'est-ce qu'elle prend comme plat principal?
   — Elle prend la pizza.

2. **Qu'est-ce que vous prenez comme entrée?**
   Je prends la soupe.
   What are you having for your starter?
   I'll have the soup.

3. **Elle prend le gâteau.**
   Il prend un jus d'orange.

Section 3 — Hobbies

Pages 24-25 — My hobbies

1. You should have matched these sentences and pictures:

Je n'aime pas la musique.   Je déteste le cyclisme.

J'aime la natation.   J'adore la lecture.

2. True, False, False, True

3. **Tu aimes les jeux vidéo?**
   No, I hate video games.

Pages 26-27 — Music

1.

n	e	a	n	r	b	u	a	c	m	l	e

é	u	n	e	a	r	b	v	a	r	n	t

e	o	n	a	n	u	y	v	e	m	u	x

s	o	u	h	w	p	s	e	g	l	r	k

2. **Tu** aimes **la** musique **folk**?
   Non, c'est ennuyeux!
   Tu **aimes** la **musique** rock?
   Oui, c'est **entraînant**!

3. **Tu aimes la musique pop?**
   Oui, j'aime la musique pop, mais je préfère la musique classique.

Pages 28-29 — Musical instruments

1.

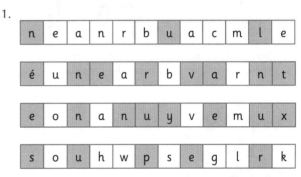

2. **Tu joues d'un instrument de musique?**
   Oui, je joue de la clarinette.
   Non, je ne joue pas d'un instrument de musique.

3. **Je joue du piano.**
   Je joue du saxophone.
   Je joue du violon.

Pages 30-31 — The weekend

1. Qu'est-ce que tu **fais** le weekend?
   Je **surfe** sur le net.
   Je **joue** aux jeux de société.
   Je **vais** au cinéma.
   Je **regarde** la télé.

2. Who does Olivier call? — **His friends**
   Where does Lucinda go? — **The park and the cinema**
   Who plays board games? — **Sylvain**
   What does Anabelle do? — **Surfs the internet and goes on the trampoline**

3. **Qu'est-ce que tu fais le weekend?**
   Je vais au cinema et je joue aux jeux vidéo.
   Le weekend, je téléphone à mes amis.

Pages 32-33 — Films

1. You should have matched these sentences and pictures:

Je veux regarder   Je veux regarder
un film romantique.   un film comique.

Je veux regarder
un film d'aventure.

2. You should have circled these words:

Tu   animer   film
regardé   je   ne
   un   la   une
      veux
   animé   dessin
regarder

Je   le   d'horreur
un   une   de
      film
action   veux   pas
   ne   d'action   regarder

Tu veux regarder un dessin animé?
Je ne veux pas regarder un film d'action.

3. **Do you want to watch a horror film?**
   Non, je ne veux pas regarder un film d'horreur.

Section 4 — A School Trip

Pages 34-35 — The wheels on the bus

1. J'entends le **klaxon**.

J'entends les **roue**s.
J'entends le **moteur**.
J'entends les g**ens**.

2. Qu'est-ce que tu **entends**?
   J'entends **les essuie-glaces** et **le bébé**.

   What do you hear?
   I hear the windscreen wipers and the baby.

3. **Qu'est-ce que tu entends?**
   J'entends le bus et le klaxon.

Pages 36-37 — On the way

1. Qu'est-ce que tu **aimes** faire dans le bus?
   J'aime bavarder **avec** mes amis.
   Je **voudrais** manger des bonbons.
   J'aime jouer **aux** jeux vidéo.
   Je voudrais **dormir**.
   J'aime **rêver**.

2. True, True, False

3. **Qu'est-ce que tu voudrais faire pendant le voyage?**
   Qu'est-ce que tu aimes faire dans le bus?

Pages 38-39 — Through the window

1. Je vois un c**amion**.
   Je vois une **vach**e.
   Je vois un **ar**b**re**.

2.

					¹v	²a	c	h	e
³m			⁴c			r			
⁵o	i	s	e	a	u	b			
u			m			r			
l		⁶v	i	l	l	e			
i			o						
n			n						

3. Qu'est-**ce que** tu vois?
   Je **vois** un feu tricolore.
   Je vois une **cabine** téléphonique.
   Je vois une boîte **aux** lettres.

Pages 40-41 — At the museum

1. You should have matched these sentences and pictures:

Il y a une armure complète.   Il y a des bijoux anciens.

Il y a une peinture.   Il y a des os de dinosaure.

. You should have circled these words:

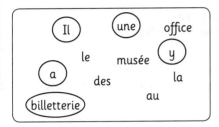

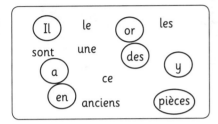

Il y a une billetterie.
Il y a des pièces en or.

3. **Qu'est-ce qu'il y a au musée?**
There is some ancient jewellery and a mummy.

Pages 42-43 — In the countryside

1. Qu'est-ce **que** tu **aimes** faire à la **campagne**?
J'aime **jouer** à **la** balle.

2. Which two people are going to draw? — **Julien and Melissa**
What is Rory going to do? — **Swim and feed a lamb**
What is Melissa going to collect? — **Blackberries**
Who is going to have a picnic? — **Noor**

3. **Qu'est-ce que tu vas faire à la campagne?**
Je vais faire du cheval et dessiner.
J'aime nager et ramasser des feuilles.

Section 5 — Seasons

Pages 44-45 — The seasons

1. You should have matched these sentences and pictures:

C'est l'hiver.

C'est l'été.

C'est le printemps.

C'est l'automne.

2. You should have ticked: une année, l'été, le printemps.
You should have crossed: l'iver, un moi, une semane.
The correct spellings are: **l'hiver, un mois, une semaine**.

3. C'est **une** année.
C'est **l'**hiver.
C'est **l'**automne.

4. Il y a sept jours dans une **semaine**.
Il y a quatre semaines dans un **mois**.
Il y a douze mois dans une **année**.

Pages 46-47 — Spring and summer

1. **Pourquoi** tu aimes l'été?
Parce que **j'aime** jouer au parc.
Qu'est-ce que tu peux faire **au** printemps?
Je **peux** voir les jonquilles.
Je peux **manger** une glace.
Parce que j'aime aller **à la** plage.

2. False, True, False, True

3. **Qu'est-ce que tu peux faire au printemps?**
I can stroke the lambs.

Pages 48-49 — Autumn and winter

1. C'est un f**locon** de neige.
C'est une **bou**le de neige.
C'est un **bonhomm**e de neige.

2. C'est **une châtaigne**.
C'est **un renne**.
C'est **un cadeau**.

3. **Qu'est-ce que tu peux voir en hiver?**
Je peux voir un sapin de Noël.
En automne, je peux voir des feuilles
rouges et une citrouille.

Pages 50-51 — The date

1. **Quelle est la date d'aujourd'hui?**
On est le dix-sept novembre.

2. Quelle est la date de ton **anniversaire**?
C'est le **neuf** janvier.
C'est le seize **février**.
C'est le **vingt-trois** mars.
C'est le **premier** juin.
C'est le douze **juillet**.

3. On est le **huit mai**.
On est le **premier décembre**.
On est le **quatorze avril**.
On est le **trente et un octobre**.
On est le **vingt-quatre août**.
On est le **vingt septembre**.

Pages 52-53 — Arts and crafts

1. Qu'est-ce **que** tu **voudrais**?
Je voudrais un **crayon** et **des feutres**.

2.

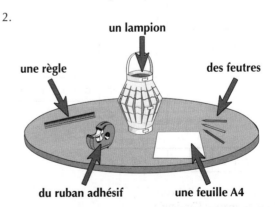

un lampion
une règle
des feutres
du ruban adhésif
une feuille A4

3. **I would like some scissors, a handle, a ruler**
and some sticky tape please.

Section 6 — The Environment

Pages 54-55 — The weather

1. **Jenny**

2. **Il y a** du vent.
   Il neige.
   Il y a du soleil.
   Il fait chaud.

3. À Marseille, il **y a** du soleil.
   À **Paris**, **il** pleut.
   À **Strasbourg**, il neige.
   À Bordeaux, il y a **du vent**.

4. **Quel temps fait-il?**
   Il pleut et il fait froid.

Pages 56-57 — The pond

1. **cra**pa**ud**
   cygne
   t**riton**

2. **Qui habite dans l'étang?**
   Qu'est-ce qu'il y a dans l'étang?

3. You should have circled these words:

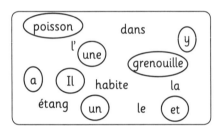

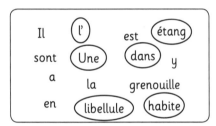

Il y a un poisson et une grenouille.
Une libellule habite dans l'etang.

Pages 58-59 — The garden

1.

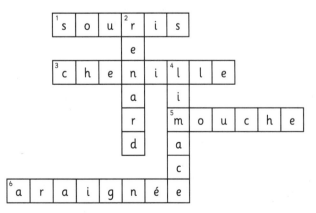

2. Le renard mange **l'oiseau.**
   L'oiseau mange l'araignée.
   L'araignée mange la mouche.

3. **Qu'est-ce qu'il y a dans le jardin?**
   Il y a un hérisson.
   L'oiseau mange quoi?
   L'oiseau mange la chenille.

Pages 60-61 — In the garden

1. You should have matched these sentences and pictures:

Je n'aime pas jouer
au badminton.

Je n'aime pas lire.

J'aime jouer dans
le bac à sable.

2. What two things does Rachid not like doing in the gard
   — **Playing football and collecting insects**
   What doesn't Lola like doing in the garden? — **Planting tr**
   What does Lola like doing? — **Playing with her pets**

3. Qu'est-ce que tu **aimes** faire dans le jardin?
   J'aime jouer **au** foot.
   Je **n'**aime pas arroser les plantes.

Pages 62-63 — Rubbish

1. C'est une **boîte** vide.
   C'est un j**ournal**.
   C'est un **boca**l en verre.
   C'est un carton à **céréa**les.

2. C'est la **poubelle** à **recyclage**.
   Je jette une **bouteille** en **plastique**.
   Je **jette** un pot à **yaourt**.

3. **Qu'est-ce que tu jettes dans la poubelle à recyclage?**
   Je jette une canette à soda.

   What are you throwing into the recycling bin?
   I'm throwing a drinks can.